Doctor Rob

The Promis Ideas on F

preventing
addiction

PROMIS

The PROMIS Primer

Written and illustrated by Dr Robert Lefever

PROMIS Recovery Centre Limited
The Old Court House, Pinners Hill
Nonington, Nr. Canterbury
Kent CT15 4LL. UK
www.promis.co.uk

First published 1998

ISBN 1 871013 15 1

Design and production by Interact, Woodbridge, England.
Printed in Basauri, Spain by Grafo SA.

To Our Children

Acknowledgements

To our patients.

To my wife Meg and son Robin for their work alongside me
in the PROMIS Recovery Centre and PROMIS Counselling Centre
helping other families.

To my secretary, Sarah Oaten.

To Amelia (6) and Celine (8) for liking my pictures.

Introduction

We all know what should work in helping children - but does it actually work in practice?

The prospect of increasing addiction in our society is frightening enough but the thought of one of our own children becoming addicted in any way is frankly terrifying. We tend to believe that it couldn't happen to us because we love our children, educate them and support them, even disciplining them when appropriate. Yet it does happen.

Then we clamour that something should have been done. The Government, the schools, the churches and the medical people should have published the message more clearly:

These things are dangerous! Don't risk it!

We get the police to give lectures on drugs and we get doctors to talk about alcohol (in the hope that children can learn to drink sensibly) and talk about the dangers of cigarette smoking (in the hope that our children won't take it up) and eating disorders (in the hope that they won't get involved in silly fads). We search for books to tell people the simple message:

These things are dangerous! Don't risk it!

Okay, I've said it twice - and in heavy type - but there is just one problem: that approach doesn't work. Let me say it again:

That approach doesn't work.

To be fair, it may have value for people who have no risk of being addicts in the first place because they lack the genetic inheritance. It is becoming increasingly clear that people do not become addicted (other than merely physically); they are probably born with that tendency. Even so, anyone can get damaged as a result of being stupid. There is therefore no harm in traditional approaches even if they do nothing for potential or actual addicts.

One significant block to the understanding of addiction is that it tends to be interpreted too narrowly (looking only at heroin and cocaine and other illegal drugs) or, alternatively, too broadly (saying that everyone has an addiction to something or, at any rate, an addictive tendency - which isn't true, although the people who are most convinced that they do not have a problem are commonly those who do).

This book is aimed primarily at children in known addictive families in order to try to help them to avoid the problems that others endured. It may not work but it's worth a try and it won't hurt other children to read it as well so that they get an understanding of addictive disease and recovery before their minds are poisoned by prejudice.

Preventing Addiction

Some people

drink **too** much,

smoke,

eat **too** much

or eat **too** little,

take drugs

or gamble,

and lose **all** their money.

They often do these things because they are **addicts**.

They didn't always behave like that:

they were young,

healthy

and happy.

Many had good jobs,

nice houses,

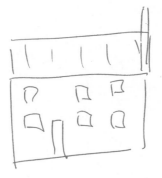

smart cars

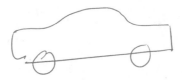

and stylish clothes.

Most had friends

and family who loved them

but they felt **empty** inside.

So they did things that made themselves feel better.

Sometimes they did sensible things, like being kind to someone

and at other times they did silly things that hurt themselves and other people.

Grown-ups sometimes think that all they have to do
to stop children becoming addicts is

to love them,

educate them

and to punish them if they do bad things.

This doesn't work.

Many children who become addicts are

much loved,

knew all about the dangers of **alcohol, drugs, food, gambling** and other addictions

and had often been punished when they did bad things

but it did not stop them.

They were told about **danger**

and **damage.**

They were even told about people who had **died from addiction**

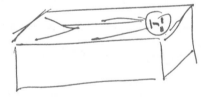

but it did not stop them.

QUESTION: Where does it all go wrong?

ANSWER: It doesn't: it's just the way some people are made.

QUESTION: What can be done about it?

ANSWER: A lot: they can learn what to do to help themselves
each day.

QUESTION: How do we know who might be addicts?

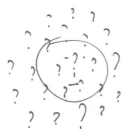

ANSWER: By looking at the way they behave with their addiction.

Addicts all tend to behave in the same way in their addiction.

1. They always have it on their minds.

2. They often use it by themselves.

3. They use it to make themselves feel different.

4. They use it as a medicine.

5. They don't want to lose any of it.

6. Once they start to use it in any day they usually go on and on.

7. They can use lots more than other people but don't seem to get hurt.

8. They go on using it even if they do get hurt by it.

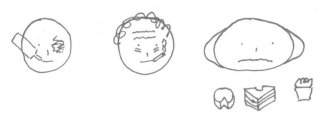

Most of all, they don't think they have a problem.

Not me

Not me

Not me

Not me

Not me

They think life is **unfair**

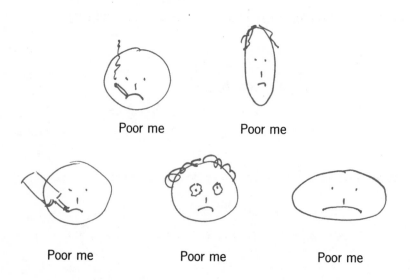

Poor me

Poor me

Poor me

Poor me

Poor me

and they **blame everyone else** except themselves.

It's his fault   It's her fault   It's their fault

It's your fault   It isn't my fault

They **get worse** as they get older.

Let's see if we can stop this before it begins to go wrong.

STOP !

Some ideas seem right but are in fact wrong:

1. Addicts are stupid.

WRONG!
Many are very clever.

2. Addicts did not know what was dangerous.

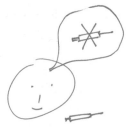

WRONG!
They did know - and
they did it anyway.

3. Addicts come from bad homes.

WRONG!
They often come
from good homes
and are much loved.

4. Addicts have been hurt when they are young.

WRONG!
Some have been hurt
but others have not -
just like other boys and girls.

5. Addicts have been led into bad ways.

WRONG!
They often went looking
for trouble. They enjoyed
the excitement.

6. Addicts learn bad things from older people and from strangers.

WRONG!
They often learn from
friends and family.

7. Addicts learn bad things from magazines and TV.

WRONG!
They sometimes do -
but they learn most of all
from each other

One idea seems wrong but may in fact be right:

Addicts are born different in some ways:

1. They come from a family of addicts of one kind or another.

2. They feel separate from other people.

3. They have big mood swings, feeling right up one time

and right down the next.

4. They try to control everything with reasons and excuses.

5. They are easily upset.

6. They are easily bored.

They often feel

lonely,

angry,

sad,

misunderstood,

picked upon

and resentful.

They sometimes

stop doing the things that they once enjoyed doing with other people

and they don't do as well at school as they did before.

They get into **trouble**

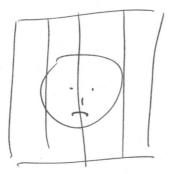

and they pick **new friends** who also get into trouble.

If **you** are like this you need to learn about addiction **before** you get into trouble.

Some children have to learn about deafness

or blindness

or disabilities

or diabetes or asthma or other illnesses

so that they can be comfortable and happy and not have problems from their disease.

You have to learn about the **inner loneliness** of addiction

so that you can be **comfortable and happy** and not have problems in future.

This book is for **YOU;** to help **YOU.**

This book is also about **me:** I am like you.

I used to **feel empty** inside.

Then I used to **eat too much, spend too much, smoke** and **gamble.**

and I **worked too hard** to try to make myself feel better.

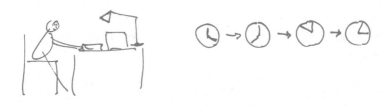

It didn't help: none of it helped:
I felt worse.

There are lots of people like you and me.

Addicts are like each other in one particular way: our brakes don't work very well.

In any day, once we start to do some things we find it difficult to stop.

That's why we drink too much, gamble, eat too much or too little,

go on smoking cigarettes or using drugs or doing other damaging things.

Eventually **we lose control.**

Other people can control these things but we can't.

We try to - and sometimes
we can, but not always -
and then we go too far
and then we get hurt again.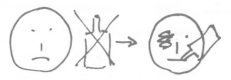

Then we try very hard to CONTROL ourselves and use our
WILL-POWER (and we may even stop for a long time).

but we get angrier   and a-n-g-r-i-e-r   and ANGRIER

So now we don't start! AND we take certain steps to keep us happy.

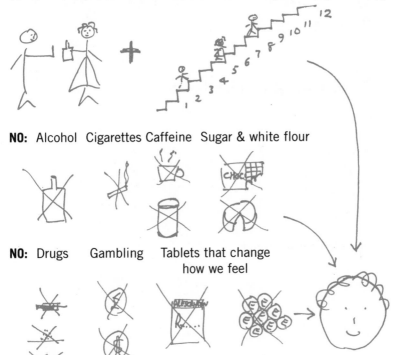

NO: Alcohol Cigarettes Caffeine Sugar & white flour

NO: Drugs   Gambling   Tablets that change
how we feel

Sometimes we have to learn to do things properly instead of doing them too much:

- we work **enough** but not too much.

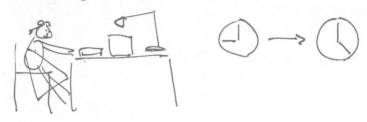

- we shop and spend **enough** but not too much.

- we exercise **enough** but not too much.

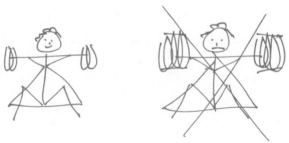

We also have to learn not to use other people to solve all our problems.

That is cheating! We have to learn for ourselves.

Also we have to learn not to solve everyone else's problems.

They have to learn for themselves! That is better for them.

It's also not good for us to be too bossy!

We have to learn to do things for the right reasons:

- we work to make things and earn money.

- we shop and spend only for the things we need.

- we take only enough exercise to keep us healthy.

We don't do these things for other reasons:

- just to change how we feel.

- or to think we are better than other people.

NOW:

if you are like us, it would be nice if you learnt not to do silly things like we did

and **not** get a lot of pain like we did.

LEARN TO SAY "NO" to things that might hurt you

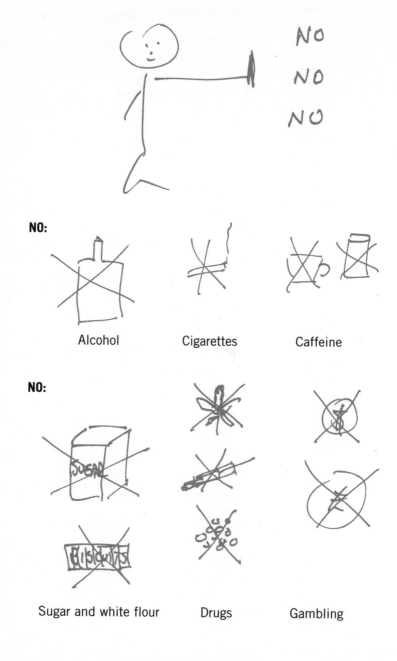

NO
NO
NO

NO:

Alcohol   Cigarettes   Caffeine

NO:

Sugar and white flour   Drugs   Gambling

and **LEARN TO SAY "YES"** to things that are really fun.

Then there's **one more thing ...**

We make special friends with other people who are like us but who do not do silly things any more.

These friends make us feel good

and we don't feel empty inside any more

And we do three things that remind us each day of what we really believe in:

1. Trust God
(any God or at least something - like Nature or Love - that is bigger than you or me).

Remember: you and I didn't make the world
and we get into a bad mess when we don't listen to good people.

2. Be honest and don't cheat!

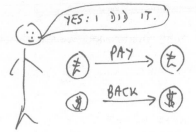

Be willing to learn.

Be kind, especially if we have hurt someone.

3. Help other people in safe and sensible ways.

We are careful not to interfere or to do things for them that they should do for themselves. They have to learn to be responsible for what they do.

When they want us to talk to them, we simply tell them:

    i.   what life used to be like for us
        (this shows them that we are like them),
    ii. what we did to change our own behaviour
        (this shows them that change is possible) and
    iii. how happy we are now
        (this shows them that they can also be happy).

When we spread happiness in the world, we are happy too.

The End
(I hope)